The Race
Meet the Merfish

Written by *T. S. Cherry*

Tiil Publishing

No Part of this publication may be reproduced, stored in a retrieval system, or transmitted in any form or my any means, electronic, mechanical, photocopying, recording, or otherwise without written permission of the publisher.

Copyright © 2013 T.S. Cherry
All rights reserved.
LCCN
Imprint Name: Pop Academy of Music

Today is the Merfish race, and the waters are crystal clear. The rules of the Merfish race are quite clear. The first rule, and the most obvious of them all, is that the first one to cross the finish line is the winner. The second rule is that the Merfish cannot use any trickery to win. They can't use their powers to slow other Merfish down or block them from progressing in the race.

After announcing the rules, Bluebell got into position. "On your marks!" Bluebell screamed out loud. The other Merfish readied themselves.

"All Merfish get set...." She raised her fin high in the air. "Let's go!" Bluebell shouted.

A colorful rainbow of musical notes lit up the sky like fireworks as the Merfish race began. The Merfish bolted from the starting line in a colorful flurry.

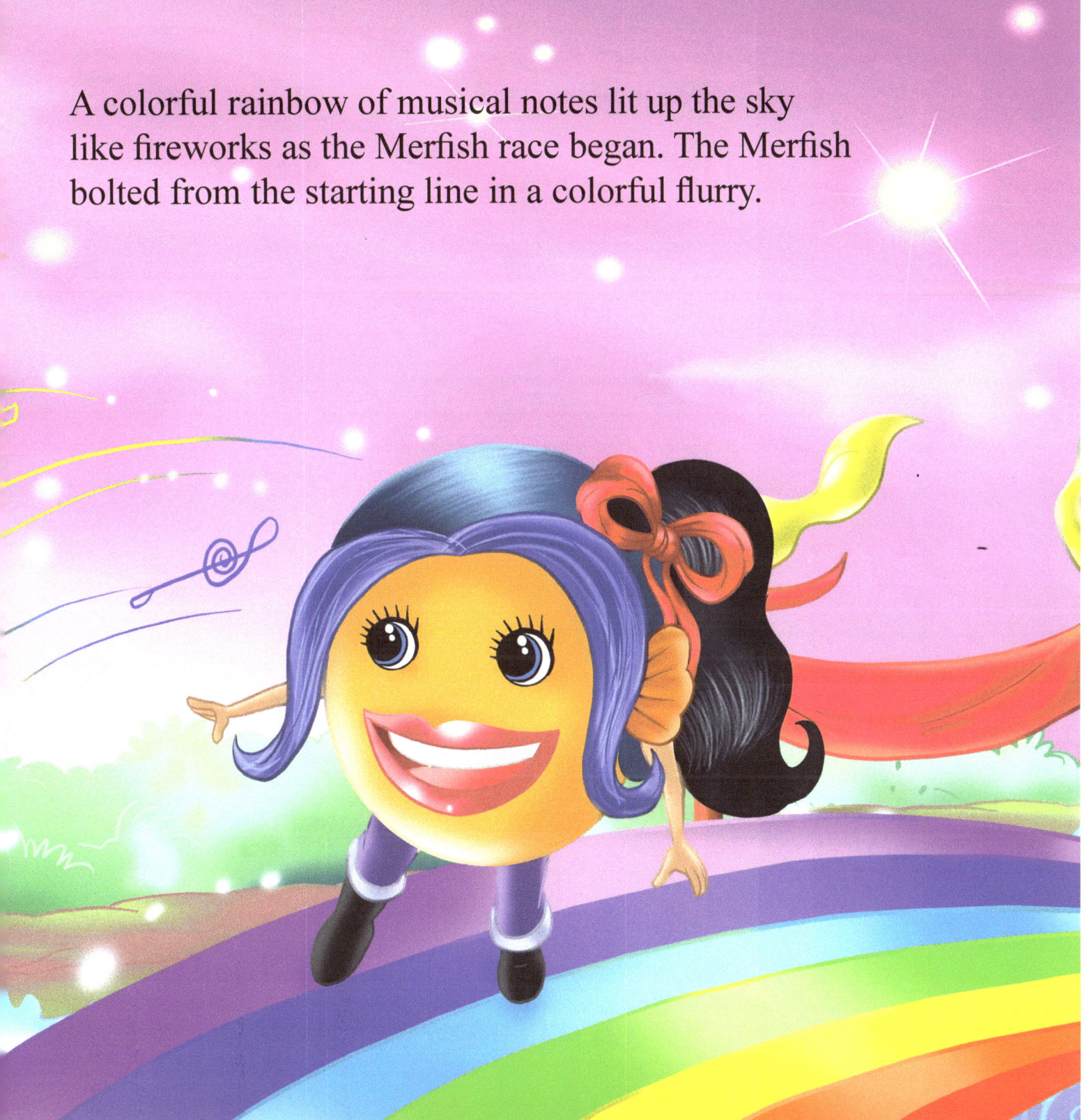

Allace used her beautiful, magical wings to get ahead in the race. She peeked behind her and spotted Bluebell just a few paces back. Bluebell was surfing a big wave that was gaining speed quickly. However, when Bluebell and Allace glanced up, they spotted Deflutter flying through the air on a magical and musical flying seahorse.

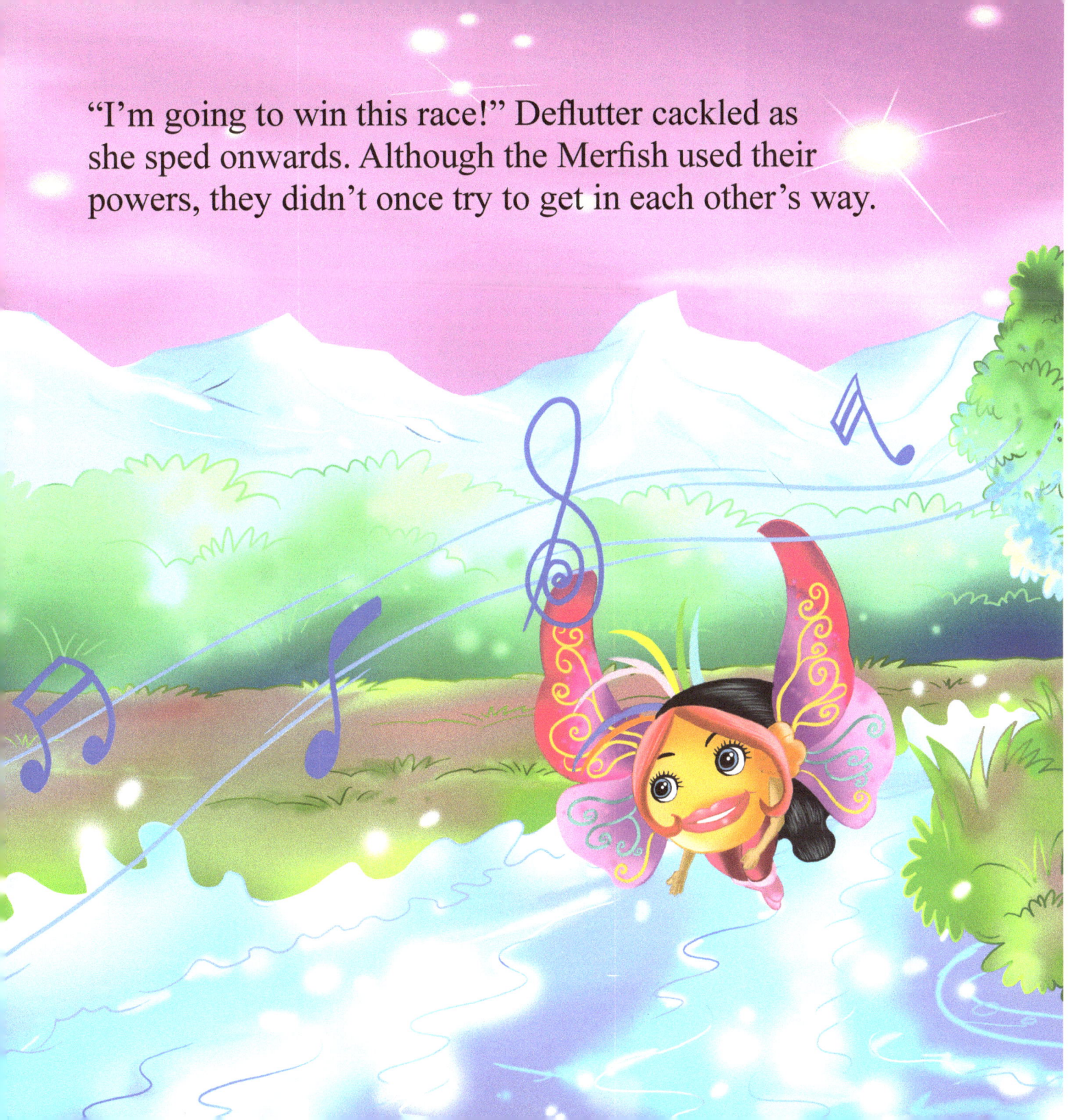

"I'm going to win this race!" Deflutter cackled as she sped onwards. Although the Merfish used their powers, they didn't once try to get in each other's way.

All of a sudden, Ivy swung by on a beautiful, thick green vine.

Above her, peering down at the groundbound Merfish, Almond Blossom soared high in a colorful balloon. "Not while I'm still around!" snickered Almond Blossom.

As Almond Blossom continued to giggle with glee, Zinna turned into a blaze of fire and took the lead for a moment.

She only held the lead for a second though, as Penny Royal sat high atop her giant butterfly.

"You need to hurry, Ivy," Bluebell said as she ran across the rainbow she had created, "or you're going to come in last place!"

Ivy laughed hysterically, thinking the notion was too silly to take seriously. "Not today," Ivy said with a snort.

Just then, something massive sped through the air.

"Coming through!" Almond Blossom yelled as she took the lead.

She sailed her big balloon past Penny Royal and giggled to herself as she thought about the finish line. She actually had a chance of winning first place, and she could almost taste her first victory!

But before Almond could enjoy her possible victory for too long, Deflutter, and her musical flying seahorse, made a sudden move.

She flew and dashed right over Bluebell and her rainbow. Next, she took the exciting lead in the Merfish race by sweeping in front of Almond Blossom and her balloon.

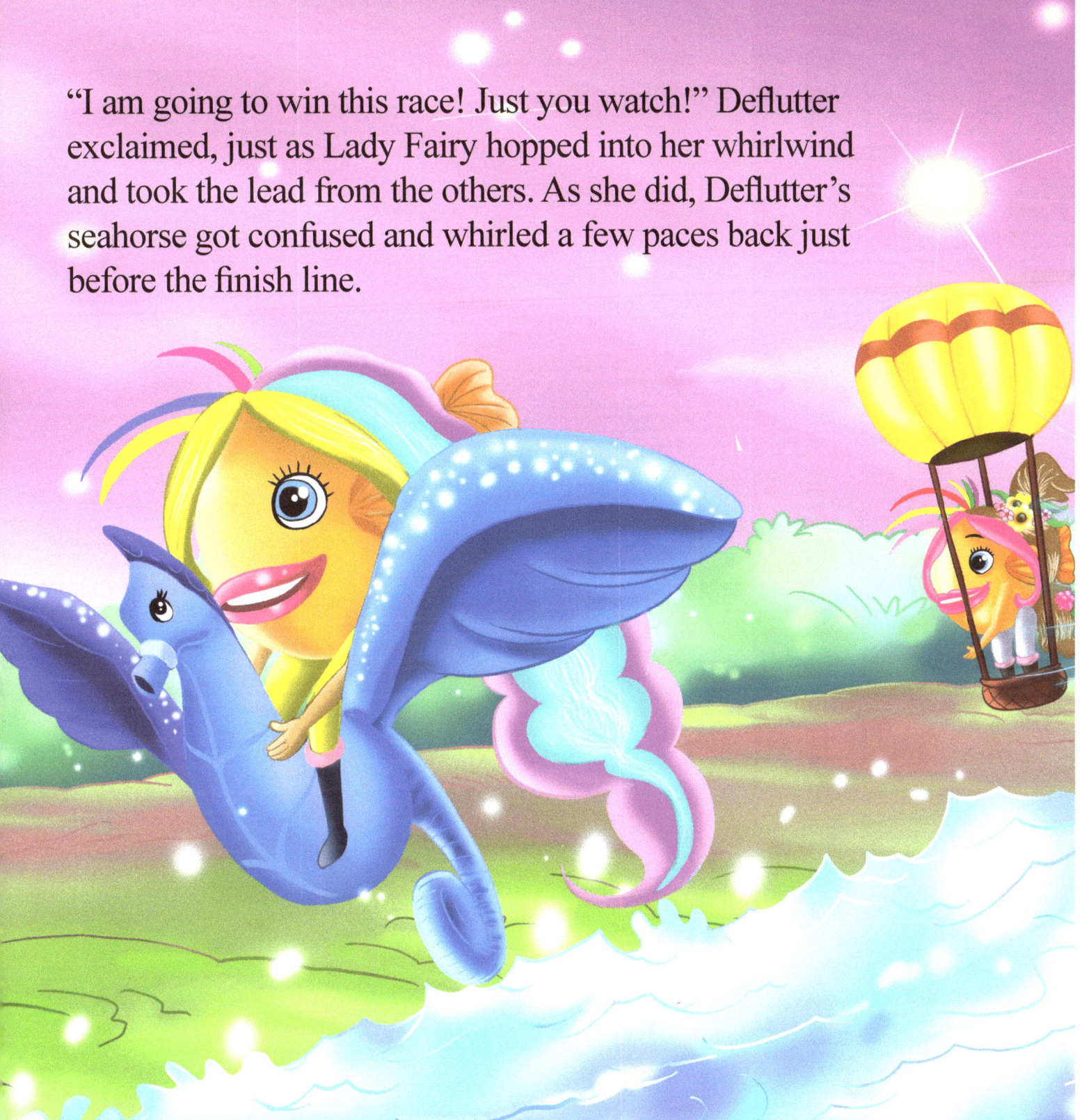

"I am going to win this race! Just you watch!" Deflutter exclaimed, just as Lady Fairy hopped into her whirlwind and took the lead from the others. As she did, Deflutter's seahorse got confused and whirled a few paces back just before the finish line.

And the votes are in! Lady Fairy takes first place, Bluebell second, Penny Royal third, and on it went. Ivy and Almond Blossom were next, with Zinna, Allace and Deflutter bringing up the rear in 6th, 7th and 8th place.

"That was such an exciting race!" Bluebell exclaimed as everyone cheered and danced about.

They were all so excited with how their Merfish race had finished. They couldn't wait for the next one to start.

Check Out Our Other Titles:

Maps the Dog

Eli Emps

Izzy the Bear

Tiger Fairy Fish

Berry Berry Bear

Parkadian Pups

Phat Cat Christmas Brat

www.ingramcontent.com/pod-product-compliance
Lightning Source LLC
Chambersburg PA
CBHW061932290426
44113CB00024B/2889